Saint Nicholas
Saint Francis of Assisi
Saint Brigid of Ireland
Saint Pachomius
Saint Anne Line

Saint Antony of Padua
Saint Monica
Saint Augustine
Saint Charles Lwanga
Saint Bernadette

Saint Ignatius Loyola
Saint Bakhita
Saint Methodius
Saint Rose of Lima
Saint Paul Miki

Printed in Canada.

Would you return to the country where you had been enslaved to tell those who lived there about Christ?

Saint
Patrick
Edgar

Patrick

patron saint of Ireland

During the time of St. Patrick, the ***Catholic church*** was lost in ***how*** to ***minister*** to the souls of Ireland. The people had been ***misled*** by the Celtic ***pagan religions*** that dominated the landscape. Sending ***help*** from European countries like ***Italy*** and ***Spain***, the Church realized its missionaries were ***restricted*** in their work by their lack of knowledge. After all, ***the missionaries*** knew nothing of the local languages nor the ***pagan beliefs*** they were there to refute.

It was ***then*** that ***St. Patrick*** stepped into the picture.

Patrick is ***accredited*** for converting Ireland as a whole to ***Christianity***, for there is no question, according to his writings, ***the Confession***, as to the ***multitudes of people*** who were ***baptized*** and saved into the grace of Jesus Christ. Fittingly, St. Patrick is now recognized as the much-beloved ***patron saint of Ireland***.

Story:
Jen Murvin Edwards

Pencils:
Edgar Salazar

Colors:
Ulises Arreola

Letters & Designs:
Keith Bahrenburg

Ireland, 409 A.D.
Wait. Stop!
Wait.
Wait for me.
What have we here?
Hello, friend. What's the trouble?
Your eyes seem to speak, yet you remain silent.

Perhaps some water will loosen your tongue. Come --
-uh-
You said it would be here, Lord ... and now, before my very eyes!
The ship. It's here!
Now you've made some noise, but you still aren't making sense.
Lads, we have a situation down here!

Thirsty?
To bring him aboard would be dangerous, John. I fear the rules --
Oh, you and rules. Let the lad tell his tale!
Then we shall see if the rules aren't worth the breaking.
Stranger, tell us what this is all about. Maybe then we'll decide to take you aboard.
My tale is long. You must grant me passage --
If I must grant you passage, then you must start talking.

ery well, sailor, but listen carefully for I've not the trength to tell it twice.
My tale begins six years ago, on a boat not unlike the one tied to that dock over there. We were captives, and I was a young lad of only sixteen years. There I met an old man ...
Least they could do is give us more food. I've begun to lose count of the days we've been at sea.
Who are these men? Who would steal people?!
The slave trade is a lucrative business. Poor souls like us fetch a load of coin, or so I've heard. Irish kidnappers, they are. They take people and sell them as slaves.
See that girl over there? I was delivering wood to a neighbor when they came -- the slave traders I mean. It was her house where ...
Where they tied us up and put us on this boat.

Never thought it would happen to me. Plucked right out of my own home, easy as a turnip from the garden.
How'd they get your family, son?
Not my family, just me.
And here I am, a slave.

The place they're from -- the place we are now headed -- is far from our homes in Gaul.
Soon we will set foot on the shores of Ireland. It is to be our new home, regardless of what we say about it.
Do you think we'll ever go back home?
Son, listen closey. What I have to say comes from the many years I have lived on this earth.
Diminish all thoughts of home, of your life as it once was, for it is no more.
To survive you must find strength in one thing -- a single source that brings you comfort, companionship and courage.
I am empty of such a source.
There you're mistaken. The source lies in each of us. In time, you will find it.
Be sure, I have never been one to give in.
That I can gather from your eyes.
What's your name, lad?
Patrick.
You're going to survive, Patrick. Be strong and you will find what you seek.

With nothing in my possession but the old man's wise words, the next morning I was taken to Antrim, where I was to meet my fate for the next six years. There I began my new life.
Yes?
We have business with Milchu.
The master -- he has been waiting for weeks.
These animals are peaceful. Perhaps there is hope after all ...
HAVE YOU COME TO SEEK MY WRATH?!
WHAT FOOL WOULD DARE BRING ME MY SLAVE THREE WEEKS PAST ITS DUE?!?
We have come not to anger you, Milchu, but to deliver what is rightfully yours ... with our apology of course.

Look your new master in the EYES!
He is near, but not yet a man.
His usefulness remains to be seen.
He will be worth his price or he will not be the only one to face the consequences.
Yes, we --
Now out of my sight!
Enter -- you will compensate me for the time I've lost on your behalf.
As soon as the door had closed, I realized that this was to be my new life.
This was my new home. And I was far from welcome.

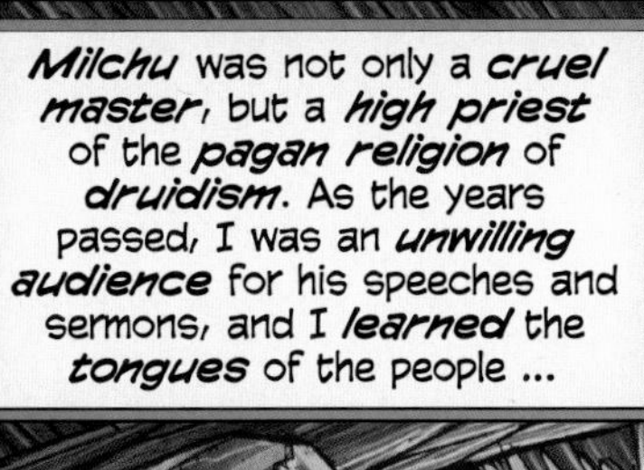
Milchu was not only a cruel master, but a high priest of the pagan religion of druidism. As the years passed, I was an unwilling audience for his speeches and sermons, and I learned the tongues of the people ...

But I also learned the language of pain.

Despite the old man's warning, I was far from home and felt every mile. I spent many nights steeped in nightmares, unable to wake ...

And when I did wake, I wished again for dreams.
Get up! There is work to be done.

But as time passed, the words of the old man continued to sit in my heart. I sought that of which he had spoken, and the Lord, hearing my knock, answered the door.
I spent my days engulfed in prayer. Though I was a shepherd, I was also a part of His flock. As I would lead my sheep to safety, my Lord Jesus Christ led me daily to His strength, peace and forgiveness.

The days passed, and my every thought was a prayer. I felt the Lord's presence both in sleep and waking.
Then one night, a voice came as it never had before ...
PATRICK ~~ PATRICK ~~ IT IS TIME FOR YOU TO GO.
A vision.
LEAVE THIS PLACE, FOR A SHIP AWAITS.
YOU MUST RUN QUICKLY. GO TO THE SHIP.
GO AND IT WILL TAKE YOU HOME.

And here I am before you. Your ship is traveling to Gaul -- of this I have no doubt.
I have heard of Milchu, your master. His land lies over two hundred miles from this dock where we now sit.
Without the Lord's hand upon me I would have never survived ... nor found my way to you this night.
We know you speak the truth, for Gaul is our destination.
And you, our guest.
He has led me to your ship. To Gaul. To home.
I take it, Patrick, these men sailed you safely to Gaul?
Yes, Benignus. From there I was reunited with the loved ones I had seen only in dreams for six long years.
Few men could have survived your adventure, let alone recovered.
And for that, even now, twenty years later, I fall on my knees in thankfulness.

ROME. circa 432 A.D.
Your story never ceases to amaze me, Patrick.
To return to your homeland and then embark abroad almost immediately to pursue studies and missions --
And now you are named Bishop by Pope Celestine himself.
Even while I rejoiced in my homecoming, I knew my time in Gaul would be short-lived. I knew I must devote my life to the Lord's service.
Patrick, there is something on your mind. Something other than your memories of oppression and pain.
I cannot deny this. Yes, even now my soul stirs with wonder at what I have seen.
Tell me, Patrick, for I am not only your disciple, but I am also your friend. I will gladly give you counsel.

Though I am grateful, I am not in need of counsel, for the Lord's intent has since been revealed to me.
But perhaps I will tell you, for this occurrence has much bearing on the journey we are embarking upon.
The incident I speak of transpired only a short time ago.
I was in Gaul, home from a mission, and seeking rest from my travels.
But rest was not the gift I was to receive that night, but a vision revealed in a dream.

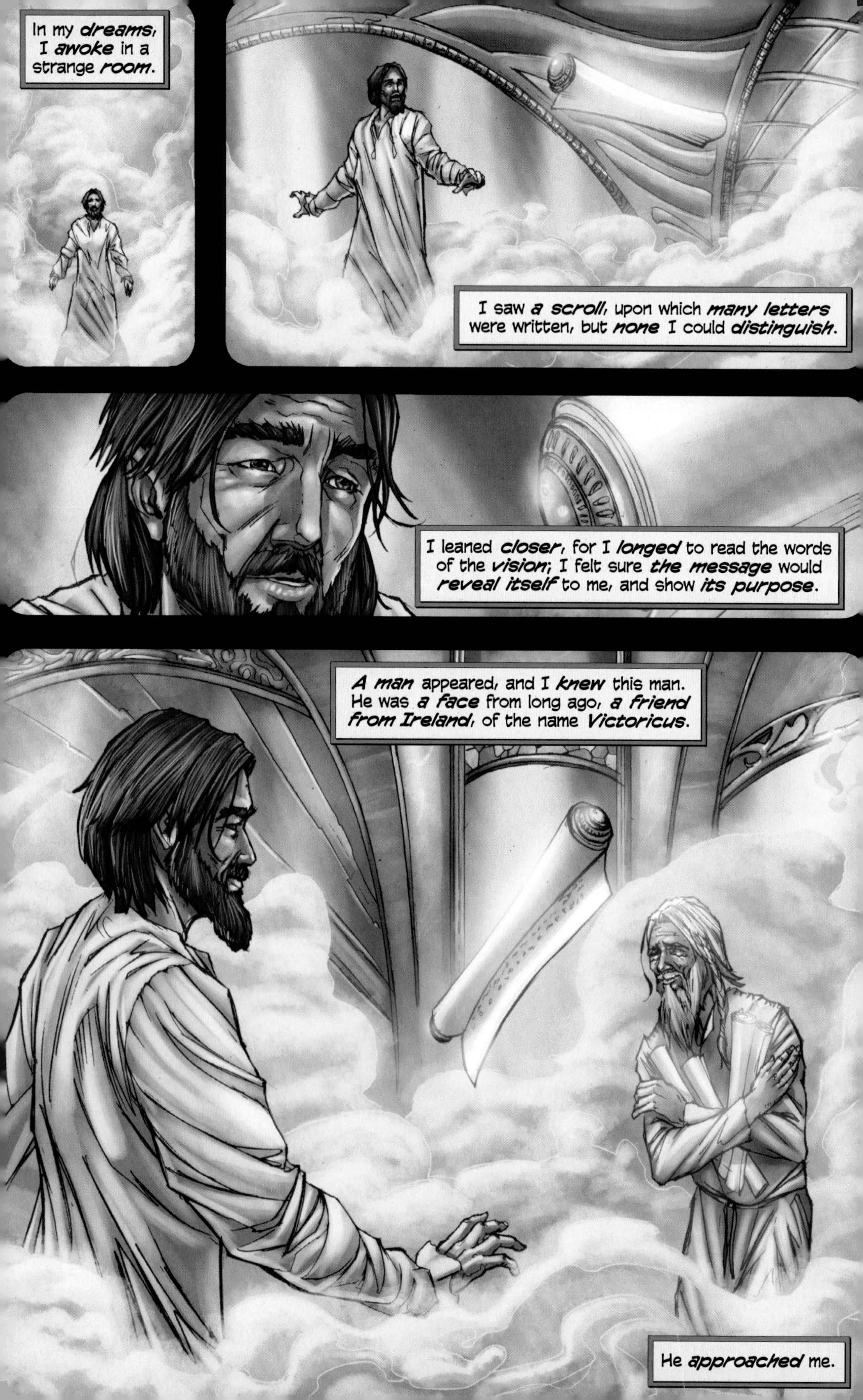
In my dreams, I awoke in a strange room.
I saw a scroll, upon which many letters were written, but none I could distinguish.
I leaned closer, for I longed to read the words of the vision; I felt sure the message would reveal itself to me, and show its purpose.
A man appeared, and I knew this man. He was a face from long ago, a friend from Ireland, of the name Victoricus.
He approached me.

My friend took hold of the scroll, and as he did so, a sound emerged from all around me.
HOLY YOUTH ...
HOLY YOUTH ...
WALK AMONGST US ONCE MORE ...
WALK AMONGST US ONCE MORE ...
HOLY YOUTH ...
WALK AMONGST US ONCE MORE ...
HOLY YOUTH ...
As I read the words, I heard Irish children. Their lilting voices rang in the air like church bells carried on a distant breeze.
The children of Ireland ... they call to me.
As soon as I gained back my breath ...
I awoke in my bedroom.
Their voices were gone.

Your story has stilled my blood, and I must set my heart to beating once more; perhaps we should begin making our way to the pier. Our ship awaits.
Of course.
I have never doubted the Lord -- His will, nor His plan.
And in your life I see His hand so clearly and His intentions, so perfectly.
As a slave in Ireland, though you were cruelly treated, you were also educated in the ways of the pagans, in their languages, practices and beliefs.
In a land where all other missionaries have failed due to misunderstandings, language barriers and blameless ignorance ...
The Lord, in his wisdom, has seen to it that you, a man well versed in the culture of Irish people and full of the knowledge of God, go back and redeem that island nation.
Yes, you are right, Benignus. The Lord was with me all along. He took the pain of that time and used it for His glory.

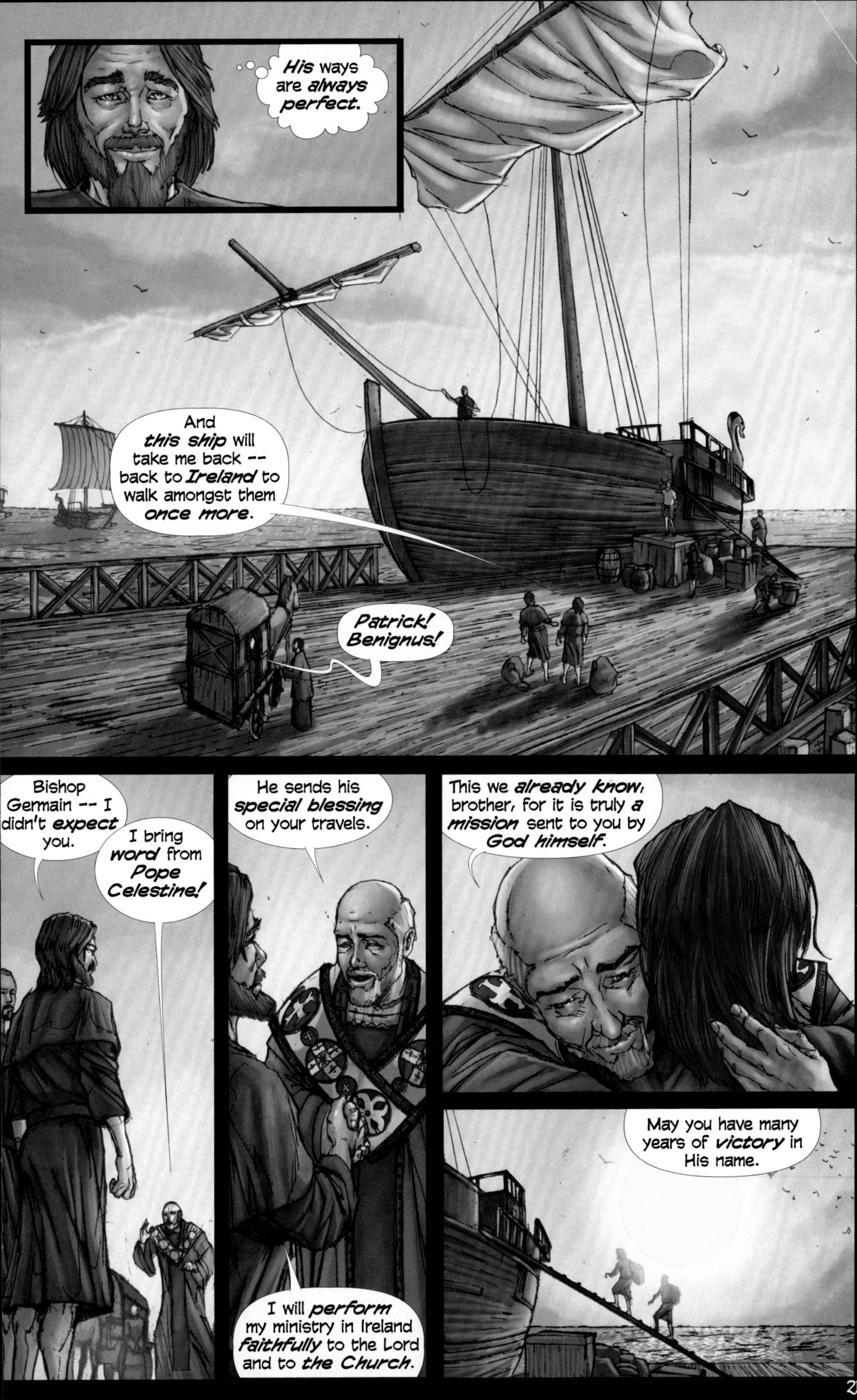
His ways are always perfect.
And this ship will take me back -- back to Ireland to walk amongst them once more.
Patrick! Benignus!
Bishop Germain -- I didn't expect you.
I bring word from Pope Celestine!
He sends his special blessing on your travels.
I will perform my ministry in Ireland faithfully to the Lord and to the Church.
This we already know, brother, for it is truly a mission sent to you by God himself.
May you have many years of victory in His name.

Ireland. 432 A.D. - circa 461 A.D.
For thirty years until his death, Patrick ministered to the people of Ireland. He preached the truth, established numerous churches and baptized countless souls.
Those he baptized began churches of their own, and Patrick's ministry grew, with himself as the root, his followers as the branches, and the Lord as the life-giving water that made Christianity thrive in Ireland.

A Saint's Journey

Circa 389 A.D.* :** St. Patrick is born of ***Roman-British origin to his father ***Calpurnius***, a deacon and municipal official, and his mother, Conchessa. St. Patrick's full name is said to be ***Patricius Magonus Sucatus***.

403 A.D.* :** St. Patrick is ***kidnapped from his home by ***slave traders*** to become a slave in the then pagan-inhabited lands of ***Ireland***. For ***six years***, St. Patrick would serve as ***a slave*** to his master while at the same time becoming ***immensely*** devout and ***religious***, praying constantly. St. Patrick himself wrote how he would say over ***one hundred prayers*** during the day and as many at night, and would often sleep on the ***mountaintop*** to do so.

409 A.D.* :** St. Patrick hears ***a voice in his sleep, which tells him to be ready to ***return to freedom***. He ***runs away*** from his master, traveling ***over 200 miles*** until he comes upon ***a ship***, which he is certain is ready to set sail to his homeland. While the sailors ***refuse*** him passage at first, St. Patrick prays a ***silent prayer***, and they ***agree to*** let him on board. The ***journey*** is long and difficult. The group ran out of provisions and St. Patrick was forced to ***go hungry*** for many days.

Circa 411 A.D.* :** St. Patrick is returned to his ***homeland, where he is happily reunited with ***friends*** and ***family*** at around the age of ***twenty-two***.

415 A.D. - 430 A.D.* :** St. Patrick studies at ***Auxerre, where he receives ***holy orders***. Meanwhile, ***Pope Celestine*** begins to send the first of many missionaries to Ireland, where they ***perpetually fail*** and/or are ***killed*** in their ministries among the ***Celtic pagans***.

432 A.D. : ***St. Germanus*** consecrates St. Patrick as ***bishop to*** replace a missionary named ***Palladius***, who was killed in Ireland. St. Patrick is charged with completing the task of ***evangelizing*** the people of Ireland and to ***finish the work*** barely started by ***Palladius***. St. Patrick ***embarks for Ireland***.

444 A.D. : Though ***most*** of the details of St. Patrick's ministry in Ireland are ***unknown***, upon ***this date*** it is said that the cathedral church of Armagh was ***founded***, and grew to become the center of education and ***administration*** for the church in Ireland.

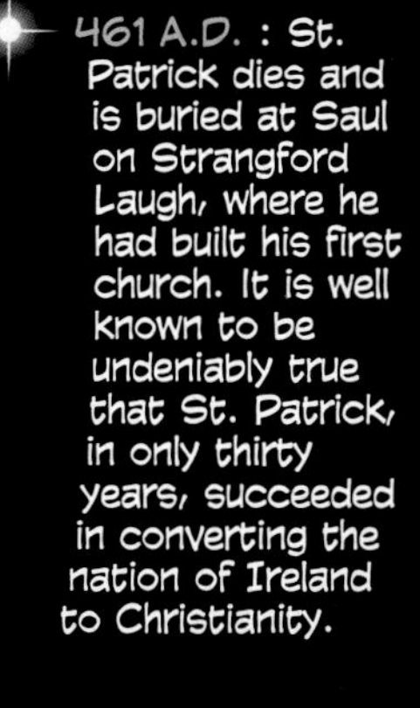

461 A.D. : St. Patrick dies and is buried at Saul on Strangford Laugh, where he had built his first church. It is well known to be undeniably true that St. Patrick, in only thirty years, succeeded in converting the nation of Ireland to Christianity.

Do you have a heart
to help those in need?

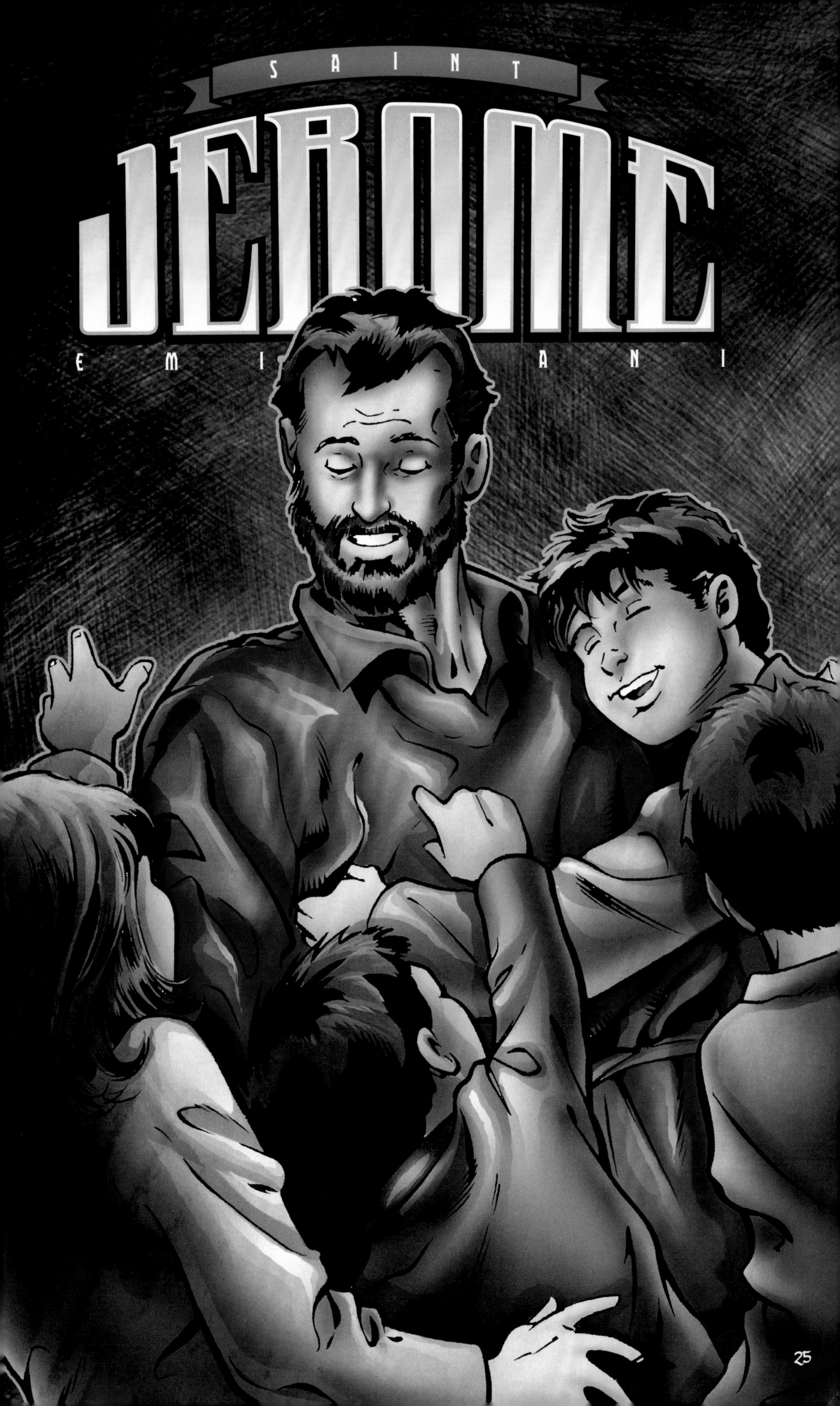
SAINT
JEROME
E M I
A N I

In 1481 *orphans* ***did not*** *have many options; left on* ***their own****, these forgotten and neglected* ***children*** *fought a* ***lonely*** *and often fruitless battle of* ***survival****. But in* ***Italy****, the life of an orphan was not the* ***death sentence*** *it could have been, for through* ***one man*** *countless children were offered* ***health, happiness,*** *and above all,* ***hope****. That man was* ***St. Jerome Emiliani****.*

A ***fierce warrior*** *before his conversion to the Catholic faith,* ***St. Jerome*** *found the* ***Lord*** *in the darkest of places. Left alone with* ***only thoughts*** *and* ***fears*** *for company, his mind and heart turned to the Lord, and he was* ***rewarded*** *with a* ***great gift****: the freedom to* ***spread*** *God's message to* ***others****.*

Because of his ***passion*** *for the* ***forgotten****, the* ***heartbroken****, and the* ***helpless****, St. Jerome Emiliani is beloved* ***internationally*** *to this day -- his influence spanning* ***generations*** *throughout Italy and the world. But* ***where*** *was this* ***dark place*** *where the Lord was revealed to Jerome, and just* ***how*** *did he change from* ***fierce warrior*** *of Italy to* ***fierce defender*** *of the* ***faith?***

Read on to discover the answer.

STORY
JEN MURVIN EDWARDS

PENCILS
KEVIN WEST

INKS
DAN DAVIS

COLORS
MIKE GARCIA

LETTERS / DESIGNS
KEITH BAHRENBURG

My name is Mario.
I'm an orphan.
That means I used to be pretty much out of luck as far as the basics go. You know, clothing, food, shelter.
But that was alright because I was tough -- AM tough.
I know my way around Venice. This city is my playground; no one knows the alleys better than me. Plus, that's how I met him.
What's Mario doing?
You know Mario. He's telling the story.
Not again!
C'mon guys, I'm trying to get some sleep here!
I always love hearing the story, though, don't you?
Yeah.
OK, we've agreed. You can go ahead and tell it, Mario. Tell the story.

Will you guys just be quiet already? OK -- here we go.
Jerome started out a kid, just like us --
Well, duh! So did everyone, Mario. Get to the good stuff! You know, when he was --
OK!
VENICE, ITALY. 1508.
So, as I was saying, Jerome started out as a kid, but he didn't stay that way long. Soon he grew up, and when he did, he joined the armies of the republic.
Commander Jerome!
Commander Jerome!
Vincento -- what is it?!
They're coming!

I was hoping for at least another day.

From the looks of it, they'll be here by midnight.
Castelnuovo will hold. This fortress is more than strong enough to withstand them.

We'll find out ... soon enough.

Yes, time will tell. But meanwhile, I want to make sure the preparations are --

Commander! We have a problem.

I found an area of weakness in the fortress!
What? Where?! Explain, quickly!

As you know, the weather has been unpredictable lately.

With all the heat and rain we've been getting, the pressure of the mud and earth have weakened the support wall.
We didn't see it earlier because we had stacked the supplies so high.
What will we do?

Let's get some men down here to help do what we can to strengthen the wall. We'll need extra troops to secure this area when night falls.

We don't have much time.

Ooooooh, this part is so exciting!
Will you be quiet? We're just getting to the good part.
OK, sorry.
Where was I?
Before they knew it, night had fallen. Castelnuovo was about to become a battleground.
Vincento! How's that wall?
Don't know, Commander! I've been a little --
Busy!
Retreat!
They've broken the outer wall!

The reinforcements -- they didn't hold!
Vincento, I want you to retreat, now!
No! I won't leave without you --
NOW!
Surrender, Commander!
Never!
It's over. Castelnuovo is ours!
I know the perfect place for you.

Well, you all know where he went.
The dungeon.

Oh, no.

Mario, *why* did you blow out the *candle?!*

Because it's *scarier* that way.

Light it again. *Light it again!*

Jerome was locked in the *dungeon* so many days and nights that he *lost count*. He was alone the *entire time*. He was not a religious man. In fact, his entire life before *this moment* had been spent *without God*.

Lord, *please* --

Please!

Now in the *darkness* Jerome *sought* the *Lord's face.*

Lord, *forgive* me for my *blindness*.

Forgive my years of ignorance --
For not knowing You, not seeing You in all things.

What? What is that?

I am not worthy, Lord. Not me.
LEAVE THIS PLACE, JEROME. THE WAY IS RIGHT IN FRONT OF YOU ...

USE YOUR LIFE TO SERVE OTHERS ...
AND IN DOING SO, YOU WILL SERVE ME.

His escape was miraculous. No one has ever been able to figure out how he could have escaped on his own.
The dungeon was impenetrable -- no going in or out -- and, except for Jerome, no one has ever escaped, before or since.

Thank you, Lord!
Thank you.

Our Lady! I give my life to you. But wait. First I must --

UNGH!

I vow myself to you, Our Lady. I offer you my chains, from which the Lord has freed me, and also my life, which I dedicate to the Lord.

And he did. After word of his miraculous escape spread, he went to Venice. Here he studied to become a priest and educated his nephews (very bright fellows, I must say, though not as street savvy as I would like).
When Jerome wasn't busy teaching or studying, he walked the poor streets of Venice. There was a lot of pain there; the plague had stricken many families.
Jerome came to know the children whose parents had died, and brought them food and water. Amongst these orphans Jerome met someone really special.
He was a big, strong man, the most intelligent in all Venice. He was so tough he could do almost anything.
Mario, I've been looking for you.
Mario -- as if we don't all know what you REALLY look like.
Mario, I've been looking for you.
Alright, fine. If you want to be picky about it.

Don't worry, it's going to be alright. I'm taking you --

gasp

I'm taking you home right now!

Is he dead?
No, just unconscious.
Will you bring me a cup of water, please?
Sure! Maybe we could throw it over his head and wake him up.

Here you go, Mario. You're going to be safe now.
What is this place?
It's a house for children like you. Children ...

Children without parents.
Yes. For orphans.

Jerome always had plans.
I want you to ask me as many questions about the Lord as you can --
Jerome didn't want us to sit around all day, though. No, he had plans for us.
Big plans.
And then I'll try to answer them. Remember what we studied last week?
Father Jerome, I've been wondering. Is God punishing us? Is that why our parents died in the plague or couldn't take care of us anymore?
What a question! Marcello, the Lord loves children. He even makes a point to tell us to take care of children like you.
"Religion that God our Father accepts as pure and faultless is this: to look after orphans and widows in their distress ..." James 1 verse 27.
The Lord gave all of this to you --
And with the Lord's help we can build more houses like this for more children.
The Lord is always with you, even when you're in the darkest of places.
Trust me ... I know.
And then it happened.

Please, Father Jerome, you're not looking well ...
I can do it, really.
I'm fine --
I --

The plague had come back to haunt us.

Father Jerome!
One of you, run for the doctor!
GO!

I ran as fast as I could. I knew it was the black death --
The plague.
Father Jerome had nursed so many people, it was only a matter of time until ...
I couldn't even think it.

What is it, boy?
It's -- it's Father Jerome, Sir.
He's got it. He's got the plague ...

Let's go!

What are you doing over here?
I couldn't stay in bed any more.
Plus this part of the story always makes me worry, even though I already know what happens.
I guess that's OK --
Let's get back to the story.
What is this?
One day, while coming up to the house, I saw a shiny seed.
I knew what I had to do. I had to feed Jerome the magic seed.
Mario! That's not what happened!
Mario, you're supposed to tell the truth. There was no magic seed! You didn't heal Father Jerome --
The Lord did.
Children -- what's going on in here?

Uh, oh!
I already saw you, Mario ...
But I haven't even gotten to the rest of the story -- the part about the other orphanages in Brescia, Bergamo, and Como --
The story?! Oh no, not again.

Don't you all have other stories to tell? You know, like dragons and fairy godmothers.
Or I think I remember a story from last week about a princess that sounded interesting ...
But those stories aren't true! Yours is.

And none of us have started any orphanages.
Or escaped a dungeon.
Or fought in sword fights!

What you haven't realized, children, is that each of you will soon have your own story to tell -- your own deeds to perform! Your own faith will testify to others!

In fact ... how about we do something really different?

Like what?
Mario, where's your candle?

Here it is.
OK, Mario. This time, I want to hear a story about you. About who you want to be -- how you're going to serve the Lord!
WOW! OK --
There once was a giant man with enormous muscles, the most intelligent man in all of Venice --
And he was so tough, he could do almost anything ...

A Saint's Journey

TIMELINE

1481: Jerome is **born** in Venice, Italy, to parents **Angelo Emiliani** and **Eleanor Mauroceni**.

1518: After a life as a **soldier**, Jerome becomes **ordained** as a priest in Venice after his **miraculous escape** from an enemy dungeon.

Really -- there was **no way** he could have gotten out on **his own**.

1531: After **recovering** from the plague, Jerome commits himself and all **personal property** to the many orphanages and hospitals he **founds** in the areas of Brescia, Bergamo, Como, and **Verona**, housing and **feeding** many orphans at his **own expense**.

1532: With **two other priests**, Jerome establishes a center of **religious training** for men in Somascha in order to **educate** new participants in his ministry. During this period, Jerome introduces the practice of **teaching Christian doctrine** to children with a catechism of **questions** and answers, thought to be the **first such** catechism of its **kind**.

Jerome always let **us** ask him **questions**, too. He said once that I ask a **LOT** of questions, but I **figure**, **how else** are you going to **find out** things?

1537: The local peasants to whom Jerome often ministered, accredit him with the gift of healing. While treating the ill, Jerome falls victim to an **infectious disease**.

February 8, 1537: Jerome succumbs to his illness and **dies**.

1767: Jerome Emiliani is canonized as **a saint**.

1928: St. Jerome Emiliani is named patron saint of **orphans** and **abandoned children** by Pope Pius XI.

QUESTIONS

St. Jerome Emiliani established a catechism written in the form of **questions** and **answers** in order to educate children.

Who made you?

That's **easy** -- **God!**

What else did God make?

Duh! God made **all things!**

Why did God make you and all things?

For His **own glory**.

How can you glorify God?

By **loving** Him and doing what **He commands**.

NOW do you see why St. Jerome's story is so **interesting?** You should really tell **your friends** about him, too. I sure **told mine**. And they all loved it.

If you lost everything,
would you still
have hope?

Saint
Elizabeth Ann Seton
mcnabb

Saint Elizabeth Ann Seton

St. Elizabeth Ann Seton was the first American-born saint of the Catholic Church. Known for her deep faith, she established schools and communities of women. Elizabeth Ann Seton continues to be an example of piety, endurance and charity.

Elizabeth converted to the Catholic faith as an adult. Having encountered the Catholic Church while in Italy, she was impacted by the Church's teaching of God's presence at the Eucharist. She longed to possess God in the sacrament and decided to convert to the faith. Her conversion, however, was harshly criticized by friends and family.

Several tragic events overwhelmed Elizabeth Ann Seton's life. Despite the deaths of close friends and family members, Elizabeth's trust in God grew. Her great faith moved her to establish the first free Catholic parochial school in America. She also founded the Sisters of Charity of St. Joseph's, the first of its kind in America, which opened schools and orphanages to serve the needy. A shrine to Elizabeth Ann Seton stands in Emmitsburg, Maryland, her home from 1809 until her passing in 1821.

story by Jen Murvin Edwards
pencils by Tod Smith
inks by Al Milgrom
colors by Mark McNabb
design & letters by Jeff Dawidowski
Jeff Dawidowski &
Adam Buechler

New York City, New York, 1780.
FATHER! FATHER, PLEASE, MAY WE READ NOW?
HOLY BIBLE
ELIZABETH! YES, I WAS JUST FINISHING UP HERE BEFORE CLASS TONIGHT.
Anatomy

IF ONLY MY STUDENTS AT COLUMBIA HAD THIS KIND OF DESIRE TO OPEN A BOOK...
AND SOON, YOU WILL TEACH ME JUST LIKE MOTHER WANTED YOU TO BEFORE SHE...

YOUR MOTHER IS LOOKING DOWN AT YOU FROM HEAVEN. SHE IS SO PROUD OF YOU.
LET'S START WITH PSALMS, SHALL WE?
YES, FATHER.

St. Paul's Church, New York, January 25, 1794.
Fourteen years later...
GOD, THANK YOU FOR THIS DAY AND FOR MY FUTURE HUSBAND, WILLIAM. PLEASE WATCH OVER US.
ELIZABETH! WHAT ARE YOU DOING OUT HERE? IT'S FREEZING! AS YOUR FUTURE SISTER-IN-LAW, I DEMAND YOU COME INSIDE AT ONCE AND MARRY MY BROTHER!
I WAS PRAYING FOR OUR LIFE TOGETHER! I'M SO GLAD TO HAVE YOU AS A SISTER-IN-LAW, REBECCA. YOU ARE TRULY A SISTER -- IN CHRIST AND IN MY HEART!
OH, STOP WITH ALL THIS! YOU'RE MAKING ME CRY, AND THE CEREMONY HASN'T EVEN STARTED YET!
REBECCA! I HAVE A FEELING THA TODAY IS THE BEGINNIN OF A WONDERFUL ADVENTURE.

New York, 1798.
Four years later...
...SO MAKE SURE TO VISIT THEM NEXT WEEK!
DEFINITELY! YOU WERE GREAT WITH THOSE KIDS TODAY, ELIZABETH.
THEY DON'T CALL YOU THE ***"PROTESTANT SISTERS OF CHARITY"*** FOR ***NOTHING!*** YOU TWO HAVE BEEN GONE ***ALL DAY!***
ANY WORD ON YOUR FATHER?
HIS ***HEALTH*** IS FADING FAST; THE DOCTOR SAYS IT WILL ***ONLY*** BE DAYS NOW.
I DON'T KNOW WHAT WE'LL DO WHEN HE PASSES. ALL OF MY BROTHERS AND SISTERS WILL BE WITHOUT A FATHER.
WE'LL HAVE SEVEN MOUTHS TO FEED -- AND THE BUSINESS -- IT'S HARD WORK.

WE'LL MAKE DO, WILLIAM. IT'S NATURAL BE CONCERNED, BUT I DON'T WANT YOU TO WORRY SO MUCH.
YOU ARE ALREADY ILL.

IT'S THE ***STRESS!*** I'M SURE IT WILL ALL WORK OUT.
GIVE IT UP TO THE LORD, WILLIAM. THAT'S WHAT I DO.

I WISH I COULD, ELIZABETH.

New York, 1803.
Five years later...
"AS THE DEER PANTS FOR STREAMS OF WATER, SO MY SOUL PANTS FOR YOU, O GOD." PSALM 42:1
WHAT DO YOU THINK THAT MEANS?
WE'RE THIRSTY?
HOW DID YOU KNOW? I WAS JUST THINKING I NEED A GLASS OF WATER! WHOA.
YOU'RE RIGHT, LITTLE SARAH! WE ARE THIRSTY. BUT DID IT SAY THAT WE'RE THIRSTY FOR WATER OR FOR SOMETHING ELSE?
SOMETHING ELSE.
THAT'S RIGHT! LIKE THE DEER NEEDS WATER TO SURVIVE, WE NEED THE LORD.
I'M NOT THIRSTY, MRS. SETON, AS MUCH AS HUNGRY.
I KNOW YOU ARE, MY DARLING. THAT'S WHY MY SISTER, REBECCA, BROUGHT YOUR FAMILY SOME MEAT AND VEGETABLES FOR A STEW.
BUT PROMISE ME, WHEN YOUR TUMMY IS FULL TONIGHT, YOU AND YOUR BROTHERS WILL GIVE THANKS TO THE LORD. HE WILL ALWAYS PROVIDE FOR YOU.

I CAN'T THANK YOU ENOUGH.
NOR WE YOU, MRS. JAMISON! I HAD A LOVELY TIME WITH YOUR CHILDREN THIS MORNING.
MY OWN CHILDREN WOULD LOVE TO GET TO KNOW THEM SOMETIME.
MAY GOD BLESS YOU BOTH. I'VE BEEN PRAYING FOR THE HEALTH OF YOUR HUSBAND, MRS. SETON.
THANK YOU. I PRAY FOR HIM AS WELL. THESE PAST FIVE YEARS HAVE BEEN DIFFICULT.
BUT GOD HAS ANSWERED OUR PRAYER. THE DOCTOR HAS RECOMMENDED ITALY FOR WILLIAM'S HEALTH, AND WE LEAVE AT THE END OF THE MONTH!
OUR DEAR FRIENDS, THE FILICCHI FAMILY, HAVE OFFERED TO TAKE US IN.
ANNA'S OLD ENOUGH TO MAKE THE JOURNEY, BUT COULD YOU WATCH THE OTHER CHILDREN WHILE WE'RE GONE?
OF COURSE! YOU KNOW I WILL. THE REST OF YOUR CHILDREN WILL BE JUST FINE WITH ME. YOU JUST FOCUS ON GETTING WILLIAM BETTER.

* These journal entries were not taken from the original texts.

Pisa, Italy, 1803.
HERE WE ARE IN ITALY! I CAN'T BELIEVE IT!
WILLIAM! ELIZABETH! ANNA!

ANTONIO, I CAN'T THANK YOU ENOUGH.
WE'LL GET YOU BETTER, MIO AMICO.
BOY, IT FEELS GOOD TO BE OFF THAT SHIP! CAN I GO PLAY, MOM?

WHAT DOES MIO AMICO MEAN?
MY FRIEND.

A few months later...
ELIZABETH! ARE YOU COMING?
SI! YES!

IN ONLY A FEW MONTHS OUR DEAR FRIEND IS BECOMING AN ITALIAN!
IT'S WONDERFUL. I HAD TO PRACTICALLY DRAG HER OUT OF TH CHURCH AFTER MASS YESTERDAY. SHE SAID SHE HAD NEVER FELT SO AT HOME!

YES, WELL, THAT COULD PRESENT A PROBLEM. WILLIAM'S FAMILY IS DEVOUT ANGLICAN.

I **FEAR** FOR HER, ANTONIO. WILLIAM'S CONDITION IS **WORSENING**, AND SHE'S GOING TO **NEED** THE SUPPORT OF HIS FAMILY,
BUT THEY WILL NOT PROVIDE FOR A CATHOLIC DAUGHTER-IN-LAW.
WHO ARE **WE** TO BE CONCERNED, BROTHER? I FEEL **GOD** HAS A GREAT PLAN FOR **OUR** ELIZABETH.
ALL WILL BE **WELL**. YOU WILL SEE.
SHE IS **PASSIONATE** ABOUT BEING A TEACHER, AND EVERYONE IS **IMPRESSED** BY HER FAITH AND DEVOTION TO WILLIAM.

LET'S **GO!** WE'RE GOING TO BE LATE FOR **MASS!**
HOLY BIBLE

DEAREST LORD, I PRAY FOR MY HUSBAND'S HEALTH AND FOR THE HEALTH OF MY CHILDREN.

MOTHER! COME QUICK! IT'S FATHER!
Later that night...
IT IS A SHAME. ELIZABETH, HE WAS A GOOD MAN.
I CAN'T BELIEVE HE'S GONE.
YOU DID ALL YOU COULD FOR HIM. WILLIAM IS IN GOD'S HANDS NOW. THANKS TO YOU, HE MADE HIS PEACE.
I AM SO GRATEFUL TO YOU AND YOUR FAMILY. YOUR FAITH IS AN EXAMPLE TO ME! I WISH SO BADLY TO ...
YOU WILL FIND A WAY, AMICA. I WILL TRAVEL WITH YOU TO AMERICA WHEN YOU ARE WELL ENOUGH FOR THE JOURNEY.
GRAZIE, THANK YOU, ANTONIO.

The Seton home, New York.
When Elizabeth arrived home, Rebecca greeted her. Elizabeth was shocked to see her dear sister-in-law so pale and ill. Rebecca passed away only a month later.
Soon after Rebecca's death, some of William's family members came to console the family, but found Elizabeth much changed.
THERE IS NOTHING BUT FEAR KEEPING ME FROM FOLLOWING MY HEART. I WANT TO CONVERT TO THE CATHOLIC FAITH. I KNOW IN MY HEART THAT'S WHAT I NEED TO DO.
IT WILL NOT BE EASY FOR YOU. I WILL PUT YOU IN TOUCH WITH BISHOP CARROLL. HE IS A FRIEND AND A MAN OF GOD. HE WILL KEEP YOU ENCOURAGED.
SHE WOULDN'T, WOULD SHE?
HOW CAN SHE CONVERT KNOWING THE CONSEQUENCES?
I SIMPLY WILL NOT BELIEVE IT -- CONVERTING!
THAT'S IT! WE'RE LEAVING. SHE'S ON HER OWN NOW.
CRASH!!
I WISH THIS ALL COULD HAVE BEEN DIFFERENT.

AM I BEING IRRESPONSIBLE TO MY CHILDREN, ANTONIO? WE NEED MY HUSBAND'S FAMILY. THEY CAN PROVIDE FOR US.
FIRST MY FATHER AND WILLIAM'S FATHER, THEN WILLIAM AND REBECCA, AND NOW MY HUSBAND'S ENTIRE FAMILY; SO MANY PEOPLE I HAVE LOVED ARE NOW GONE.
I KNOW I SHOULDN'T FEEL DISCOURAGED. I HAVE TO BE CONFIDENT THAT GOD'S LOVE WILL BE ENOUGH TO SEE US THROUGH THIS!
ELIZABETH, YOU HAVE A HEART FOR GOD, MORE THAN ANYONE I HAVE EVER SEEN!
YOU HUNGER FOR HIM. YOU HUNGER FOR THE FAITH OF THE CHURCH! ELIZABETH, MY FAMILY AND ALL OF THE FAMILIES WHO LOVE YOU IN ITALY WILL PROVIDE FOR YOU!

YOU ARE RIGHT, MIO AMICO. I TOLD A LITTLE GIRL THE SAME THING ONCE. GOD WILL ALWAYS PROVIDE.
SWOOOSH!!

St. Peter's Church, March 1805.
HOLY BIBLE

* This letter is not the exact words of Elizabeth Seton.

WELCOME, STUDENTS!
WELCOME TO YOUR FIRST DAY OF SCHOOL!
YOU ARE HERE TO RECEIVE AN EDUCATION. BUT THE MOST IMPORTANT THING YOU WILL LEARN HERE IS NOT READING, WRITING OR ARITHMETIC.
SISTER, THEN WHAT IS IT WE WILL LEARN?
YOU WILL LEARN OF YOUR FATHER, MY GIRL. OF THE SACRAMENTS, OF THE WORD AND OF THE CHURCH!
LET'S BEGIN.
HOLY BIBLE

Baltimore, Maryland, 1809.
One year later...
SISTER SETON! MAY I SPEAK WITH YOU?

IS IT *TRUE*, SISTER? HAVE YOU MADE THE VOWS OF *POVERTY, CHASTITY* AND *OBEDIENCE?*
IT *IS* TRUE. I MADE MY VOWS PRIVATELY TO *ARCHBISHOP* CARROLL.

SO, YOU ARE NOW *MOTHER* SETON. THE SISTERHOOD WE'VE SPOKEN OF, WILL IT BECOME A *REALITY?*
WE CAN FINALLY DO ALL THE THINGS WE'VE *DREAMED* OF AND PRAYED ABOUT.

St. Joseph's Academy was the first free Câtholic parochial school in America. St. Elizabeth Ann Seton founded and led the Sisters of Charity of St. Joseph as superior for a number of years. The sisters worked in service to the poor, orphaned and any others in need.
I HAVE A FEELING THIS IS GOING TO BE THE BEGINNING OF A *WONDERFUL* ADVENTURE!
Elizabeth's many journals and letters are a testimony to her great devotion to God and the Câtholic faith. Though she suffered greatly at the loss of so many of her loved ones, she remained faithful and encouraging. She passed away in 1821. Elizabeth Ann Seton was the first American to be canonized by the Câtholic church.

A Saint's Journey
1774
ELIZABETH ANN BAYLEY IS BORN INTO A PROMINENT ANGLICAN FAMILY IN NEW YORK CITY.
1777
ELIZABETH'S MOTHER DIES.
1795-1802
WILLIAM AND ELIZABETH HAVE FIVE CHILDREN: ANNA MARIA, WILLIAM, RICHARD, CATHERINE AND REBECCA.
1798
ELIZABETH DISCOVERS HER LOVE OF TEACHING AS SHE ASSISTS IN THE EDUCATION OF HER YOUNGEST SISTERS-IN-LAW. THE FAMILY ENDS UP GOING BANKRUPT AND ARE FORCED TO SELL THEIR HOME. WILLIAM BEGINS SHOWING SIGNS OF TUBERCULOSIS.
1803
ELIZABETH, WILLIAM AND ANNA MARIA SET SAIL FOR ITALY IN A LAST STITCH EFFORT TO BRING HEALING TO WILLIAM'S CONDITION. THEY WERE NOT SUCCESSFUL. WILLIAM DIED AS WELL AS THEIR DAUGHTER ANNA MARIA FROM A BOUT WITH TUBERCULOSIS.
1804
ELIZABETH RETURNS TO THE UNITED STATES. DURING HER TIME IN ITALY, SHE BECOMES CATHOLIC.
1808
ELIZABETH TRAVELS TO MARYLAND WITH HER CHILDREN AND SERVES AS SCHOOL MISTRESS.
1810
ELIZABETH OPENS SAINT JOSEPH'S FREE SCHOOL IN EMMITSBURG, MARYLAND WHICH BECOMES THE SUPPORT NETWORK FOR CATHOLIC EDUCATION IN THE UNITED STATES.
1821
ELIZABETH DIES IN EMMITSBURG, MARYLAND.
1975
ELIZABETH IS CANONIZED AS A SAINT.

Would you go to a country where you could possibly be imprisoned for telling others about the gospel?

Saint Henry Morse

Saint Henry Morse

STORY:
Jen Murvin Edwards & Roger Brown

PENCILS:
Gordon Purcell

INKS:
Terry Pallot

COLORS:
Josh Ray

LETTERS & DESIGN:
Jeff Dawidowski

Perseverance.
Determination.
Devotion.
Sacrifice.

THESE WORDS EXEMPLIFY THE LIFE AND CHRISTIAN WALK OF ST. HENRY MORSE.

A HUMBLE CHRISTIAN SERVANT IN A TIME OF RUTHLESS DICTATORS, LETHAL PLAGUES AND RELENTLESS RELIGIOUS PERSECUTION, ST. HENRY MORSE WAS NO STRANGER TO FEAR. STANDING AGAINST THE MANY FACES OF DEATH, THIS HEADSTRONG PRIEST REFUSED TO BE DETERRED IN HIS CALLING TO SERVE HIS COUNTRYMEN, THE PEOPLE OF ENGLAND.

SACRIFICING HIS OWN FREEDOM, HEALTH AND, EVENTUALLY, LIFE, ST. HENRY MORSE LIFTED THE SUFFERING SOULS OF ENGLAND ABOVE HIS OWN, AN ENDURING EXAMPLE OF THE POWER OF LOVE, SERVICE AND CHRIST'S COMFORT IN TIMES OF TRIALS BOTH GREAT AND SMALL.

Rome, Italy. 1624.
Upon embarking for London, England.
WELL, HENRY, YOU LEFT ENGLAND A LAWYER AND NOW RETURN A PRIEST!
I WISH YOU SAFE HOMECOMING. BEWARE OF ENEMIES. THE KING OF ENGLAND DENIES HIMSELF SUBJECT TO ANYONE -- EVEN GOD HIMSELF.
If I had known then, Lord ...
If I could have foreseen ...

Would I have worn such cheer?

Would it have sweetened the sight of Rome's beautiful shore to know it was the last time my eyes would rest upon it?

YOU MUST BE A LOVER OF RISK, FRIEND, TO WEAR YOUR RELIGION SO OPENLY.
CATHOLIC PRIESTS ARE NOT WELCOME IN ENGLAND, TO SAY THE LEAST.
I AM NOT FEARFUL.
ALL THE SAME, STRANGER,
COME LANDING, YOU MAY FIND YOURSELF WISHING YOU HAD STAYED ON THIS SHIP, FAR AWAY FROM THE HILLS OF NEWCASTLE.
Would I have turned back?

The waters of Newcastle, England.
LAND IS SIGHTED!
PREPARE THE SHIP!
INFORM ALL PASSENGERS -- ENGLAND APPROACHES!

I know now that life is unexpected. I learned this the moment I stepped foot back in England ...
Much was not as I had left it.

STATE YOUR NAME AND BUSINESS, TRAVELER.
I AM A PRIEST ON A MISSION OF THE LORD.

YOU ARE A BOLD MAN, BUT THIS IS NOT ROME, TRAVELER, AS YOU MAY NOW REALIZE.
THE KING PRESERVES SPECIAL HOUSING FOR PRIESTS SUCH AS YOURSELF. THE JUDGE WILL SEE TO THAT.
OH --
AND WELCOME TO NEWCASTLE.

THIS MAN IS A PRIEST, JUDGE.
AND HE HAS ADMITTED THIS?
YES, WITH PASSION IF NOT FOOLISHNESS.

Yes, things in England had changed ...
THERE WILL BE NO NEED FOR YOU TO DEFEND YOURSELF.
BUT I --
YOUR TREASON ITSELF SPEAKS VOLUMES.

And not for the better!

My protests fell upon deaf ears.

And my destination had been changed.

Only hours after I landed upon the shores of my homeland ...
I entered the Castle at York with a three-year sentence ... and an uncertain future.

But only months later You rewarded my faith, Lord, and sent me a miracle.
BUT WAIT -- THERE MUST BE SOME MISUNDERSTANDING, I --

BROTHER, DO YOU KNOW WITH WHOM I MUST SPEAK ABOUT THIS SENTENCE?
YOUR WORDS WILL ACCOMPLISH NOTHING DOWN HERE ...
BUT IF YOU WISH TO APPEAL TO THE POWERS ABOVE, THAT PRIEST MAY BE OF SERVICE TO YOU.

A FELLOW PRIEST? HE WILL KNOW WHAT IS TO BE DONE.
SURELY IT MUST BE HIS VOICE I HEAR PRAYING AT THIS VERY MOMENT.
WAIT! I RECOGNIZE THAT VOICE. COULD IT BE?

YES, IT IS YOU, HENRY MORSE!
And indeed, Lord, in the darkest of times, You brought me hope.

BROTHER JOHN?! THE WAYS OF THE LORD ARE MYSTERIOUS, FOR WE HAD PRAYED TO MEET AGAIN!
AND IN HIS PLAN WE WILL REJOICE IN EACH OTHER'S COMPANY!
COME, FOR WE HAVE MUCH TO DISCUSS.

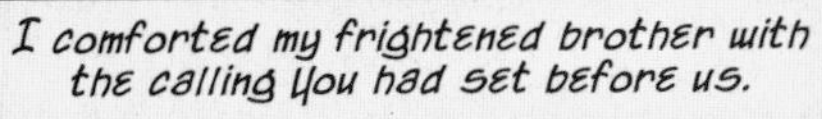
I comforted my frightened brother with the calling You had set before us.

And turned his eyes to our fellow captives.

COME -- LET US LIGHTEN OUR HEARTS!
FOR IN THE LORD'S GREAT MERCY, HE HAS BROUGHT US TOGETHER ...

AND THERE ARE MANY SOULS TO REACH.

We prayed to You then as I do now, Lord, in thankfulness and reflection.
I had no way to know that after our time in prison together, I would never see Brother John again.

EACH PRISONER WILL BE RELEASED ON CONDITION OF BANISHMENT FROM ENGLAND --
OR FACE THE PENALTY OF DEATH.
COULD IT BE?
AFTER THREE LONG YEARS, OUR PRAYERS HAVE BEEN ANSWERED!

HENRY, I KNOW YOUR HEART BELONGS TO THE PEOPLE OF ENGLAND, BUT YOU ARE BANISHED.
YOU CANNOT STAY HERE.
REGRETFULLY, I KNOW I MUST LEAVE ENGLAND ...
FOR NOW.
BUT CERTAINLY, MY WORK IS NOT OVER YET.

I parted from my brother with a heavy heart, but our paths were no longer one.
RAMSGATE
I set off alone ...

JOURNEY TO FLANDERS! ALL ABOARD!
For my journey had just begun.

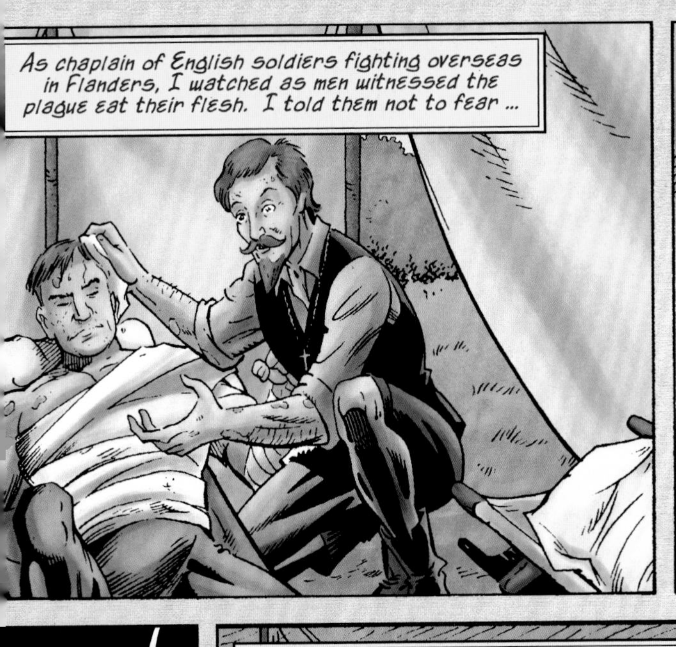
As chaplain of English soldiers fighting overseas in Flanders, I watched as men witnessed the plague eat their flesh. I told them not to fear ...

And told myself the same, even as death covered my skin like a mask.
FATHER HENRY, ARE YOU ALRIGHT?
FATHER HENRY?!

HENRY ... HENRY ... WAKE UP.

Finally, I awoke. This was to be the first of the three times I was to survive the plague.
As I recovered, Your Word comforted my heart and those around me.
LET US BE ENCOURAGED, BROTHER. REMEMBER THE WORDS OF PSALM 30:2.
"O LORD MY GOD, I CALLED TO YOU FOR HELP ..."
"... AND YOU HEALED ME."

FATHER HENRY? HENRY MORSE?
YES?
I BEAR NEWS FROM LONDON.

THE PARISH OF ST. GILES IS IN NEED. THEY ARE FACING MUCH PERSECUTION AND HAVE REQUESTED YOUR HELP.
I knew my banishment forbade me to return to England upon penalty of death ...

But I feared more the deaths of my brothers and sisters in my absence.
I WILL CHANGE MY NAME TO AVOID ARREST.
NOW WE MUST DEVISE A PLAN TO DISTRACT THE GUARDS AT PORT.

STATE YOUR NAME AND BUSINESS, TRAVELER.
CUTHBERT CLAXTON IS MY NAME, GOOD SOLDIER, AND --
CLUCK CLUCK CLUCK
CLUCK
ARRRGGH!
-- WHO IS RESPONSIBLE FOR THIS?! --
CLUCK
CLUCK
CLUCK
CLUCK
CLUCK
SOLDIER, IF I MAY CONTINUE ON ...
YES, YES -- JUST GET OUT OF HERE! SOMEONE TAKE CARE OF THESE CHICKENS!
CLUCK

SAFE JOURNEY, MR. CLAXTON!
CLUCK
And what a plan it was, Lord. One I shall never forget!

It was true; St. Giles was in great need.
Though they did suffer persecution, it was not in the form I had expected.

For the soldiers could not kill as fast as the plague.

I was grateful for what little medicine there was available, and shared it with as many families as I could.

Many were saved ...

But many were also called to Your side.

Both of our enemies -- the plague and the soldiers -- remained watchful.
FATHER MORSE?!
IT COULDN'T BE!
YOU THERE! STOP IMMEDIATELY!
YOU ENTER ENGLAND A BANISHED MAN AND FOR THIS, YOU WILL PAY!
Prison was becoming a second home to me, whether I liked it or not.

As always, You were there in the faces of men lost and searching for hope.
In their prayers they found their freedom ...
And through the orders of Queen Henrietta, You gave me mine.
IN THANKFULNESS FOR THE TREATMENT OF THOSE SICKENED BY THE PLAGUE, HENRY MORSE IS THEREBY RELEASED.
BUT BE WARNED, PRIEST. YOUR BANISHMENT STANDS. RETURN TO ENGLAND ONCE MORE, AND YOU WILL BE HANGED.

My obedience lasted for three months before I returned to England.

For I could not sit idle as the plague pulled children from their families like weeds from a garden.
I CAN'T THANK YOU *ENOUGH.* FATHER MORSE, YOU HAVE *SAVED* OUR SON.
IT IS THE *LORD* YOU MUST THANK, NOT I.

The Church of Cumberland offered me shelter.

And in return, I offered my service.

WELL, YOUNG MAN, IF YOUR RECOVERY CONTINUES IN THIS MANNER, YOU'LL BE CAUSING YOUR POOR MOTHER TROUBLE ANY DAY NOW!

YOUR SON HAS A STRONG WILL. WITH THE LORD'S HELP, HE WILL RETURN TO FULL HEALTH. GOD BLESS YOU!
But this peace was not to last.

IS THAT WHO I THINK IT IS?

The woods hold creatures far more dangerous than animals.
SEIZE HIM!!
YOU ARE A TRAITOR TO THE KING! A CORRUPTOR OF THE FAITH!
NO!

I DO *NOTHING* BUT SERVE MY COUNTRYMEN AND SPEAK THE *TRUTH*. *WHAT* IS MY *CRIME?!*
YOU HAVE CONVERTED SOULS FROM THE RELIGION OF THE STATE. FOR *THAT*, YOU WILL BE *PUNISHED!*

THE HOUR IS *LATE.* WE HAVE DALLIED TOO LONG.
WE HAD TO *EAT*, DIDN'T *WE?!*
WELL, *SOME* OF US, ANYWAY ...
The words of Jesus gave me strength.
"MAN DOES NOT LIVE ON BREAD ALONE." LUKE 4:4.

They rejoiced in my misery, laughing as the night grew darker.

I *TOLD* YOU -- IT IS GETTING *MUCH* TOO DARK.
MY HOUSE IS NEAR.

WE WILL STAY *HERE* FOR THE NIGHT.

SON, GO TO THE CELLAR AND FETCH US SOME WATER.
YES, FATHER.

A PRISONER -- HERE? I CANNOT ALLOW THIS!
HIS CRIME IS THAT OF CONVERTING SOULS TO CATHOLICISM. HE IS A PRIEST. THOUGH HE IS A CRIMINAL IN THE EYES OF ENGLAND, I'M SURE HE WILL DO US NO HARM.

HUSH -- YOU MUST NOT MAKE A SOUND.

WHY DO YOU HELP ME?
I, TOO, AM A MEMBER OF THE CHURCH. IT IS A GRAVE SECRET ...
I LIVE IN FEAR EACH DAY THAT MY HUSBAND WILL DISCOVER ME.

THE LORD SENT YOU TO ME THAT I MAY PROVE MY FAITHFULNESS.
GO. IT WILL SEEM THAT YOU HAVE FREED YOURSELF.
THANK YOU ...

MAY THE LORD WATCH OVER YOU.
Your children serve each other, Lord, with strength only You can provide.

LORD, ONCE AGAIN YOU SPARED MY LIFE. I WILL NOT LET IT GO TO WASTE.

For six weeks my freedom served the poor, but as I moved in areas unfamiliar, I relied on others for guidance.
If I had been more observant, more careful with this man's directions to the next house in need ...

Would I still have lost my way?

EXCUSE ME, SIR, BUT COULD YOU HELP --
COULD IT BE?! YES!
I KNOW YOU!
LET ME HELP YOU ON YOUR WAY TO JAIL!
WHACK!!
YOU ESCAPED FROM ME ONCE, AND THAT SHALL BE THE LAST TIME.
I know now that I was not lost, but found, for You had finally decided to call me home.

My crime was returning to England an exiled man. The court was forced to disregard my service to the English people.

YOU HAVE BEEN GRANTED LENIENCY BY THIS COURT MANY TIMES OVER, YET YOU CONTINUE TO DEFY YOUR BANISHMENT.
I COULD NOT DENY MY BRETHREN MY SERVICE. I COULD NOT LET THEM SUFFER ALONE.

MY JUDGMENT MUST BE GUIDED BY THE LAW.
IT IS TRUE -- HIS BENEVOLENCE HAS SERVED THOUSANDS.

IT IS DECIDED.
HENRY MORSE, YOU ARE FOUND GUILTY. FOR YOUR CRIMES THE PROPER SENTENCE WILL STAND ...
DEATH BY HANGING.
The court's eyes spoke of a terrible burden. For though I had served their people well, I was still a criminal in the eyes of the law.

Tyburn, England. February 1, 1645.
HENRY MORSE, YOU ARE SENTENCED TO DIE BY THE COURT OF OLD BAILEY.
Would I have turned back, knowing all I know now?
Never.
YOU MAY SPEAK ANY LAST WORDS, PRISONER.
TODAY I DIE FOR MY RELIGION. IN THE TRUTH OF GOD, I HAVE WORKED ONLY FOR THE WELFARE OF MY COUNTRYMEN.
WHILE I PRAY FOR MY SOUL TO JOIN MY LORD IN HEAVEN, I PRAY ALSO FOR THE SOULS OF MY PERSECUTORS AND FOR THE COUNTRY OF ENGLAND.
MAY GOD FORGIVE US AND GRANT US PEACE.
Henry Morse was executed in front of both persecutors and supporters. Ambassadors from Spain, Portugal and France were present in order to honor Henry Morse and his sacrifice for the Catholic Faith.

A Saint's Journey

1595
1618
1624
1627
1633
1636
1636
1641
1643
1644
1644
1645
1645

1595: Henry Morse is born in Norfolk, England and is raised a Protestant.

ca. ***1618:*** Henry is converted to Catholicism while studying law and is received into the Church at Douai, France.

ca. ***1624:*** Father Morse is ordained a priest in Rome; upon returning to Newcastle, England he is arrested and imprisoned at York Castle.

1627: Father Morse takes his vows for the Society of Jesus in England from Father John Robinson, is released from prison and leaves for Flanders where he serves English soldiers as chaplain.

1633: Father Morse returns to England under the name Cuthbert Claxton and serves victims of the plague.

1636: Father Morse is convicted of being a priest but is pardoned by Queen Henrietta Maria.

1636-1637: Father Morse falls victim to the plague three times.

1641: Father Morse is again banished from England along with all Catholic priests.

1643: Father Morse returns again to England.

1644: Father Morse is arrested but freed by the Catholic wife of one of his captors.

1644: Father Morse is again captured and taken from Newscastle to London.

1645: Father Morse is brought to the bar of Old Bailey and sentenced to death for his conviction in 1636.

February 1, 1645: Father Morse celebrates a votive Mass of the Most Holy Trinity and is taken to

Do you live a life that encourages others to follow God?

Saint Joan of Arc

Joan of Arc

As a young girl, **St. Joan of Arc** loved God and spent much time in prayer. She also loved her country – **France.** At the time of Joan's birth, **England** was occupying large parts of France. When the French king Charles VI died, an English king was crowned to rule France, instead of his son Charles VII. These events greatly impacted Joan of Arc.

God used Joan of Arc's deep **faith** and **loyalty** to reveal His plan for her life. Through visions, Joan was called to drive the English out of France. Her courageous obedience brought victory to France, and **Charles VII** was crowned the rightful king. Joan of Arc's commitment to God and country eventually cost her life, but her deep faith remains an **inspiration** to this day and her loyalty made her a national **heroine** of France.

Story: Jen Murvin Edwards

Art: Jason Millet

Lettering: Keith Bahrenburg

Designs: Keith Bahrenburg & Adam Buechler

The village of Domrémy, France. 1429.
-Gasp!-
Talk to me, please! I don't know if I'm the one, I don't know if I can do it ...
Ask Him again, Joan. Ask Him for a horse and men to accompany you to see Charles VII.
You will lift the siege on Orléans. Do not be afraid. You are not alone.
Thank You, God. I will do as You say.

A few hours later ...
Cousin? It's **Joan!** **Open** the door.

Oh no, Joan. **Not** again! Didn't you **learn** from **last time?** Captain de Baudricourt is **not** going to **listen!**

I have already tried to tell the Captain how you are **spoken** to by **God**, by the saints, and that you are to **protect Orléans** from the English.
He **mocked** you, **Joan!** And me. He told me to take you **home** and have your father give you a **good whipping!** And now you want to go **back?!**

The Captain told you Orléans **wasn't** even **under siege**. But it is now, dear Cousin. **Just** like I was told.

Told by your **voices?**
Yes. Durand, they **speak** to me. The saints talk to me as clearly as **I** talk to **you** right now. They are from **God**.

You've **convinced** me, Joan. I just hope you can do the **same** with **Captain de Baudricourt.**

ucouleurs, France. Headquarters of Captain Robert de Baudricourt.
is is ridiculous! This rm girl has the nerve to come back here again!
She did say that Orléans was to fall under siege. And now it has ...
True. But the whole country is being overrun by English!
Exactly, Sir. If I may say so, I think we should hear what this girl has to say.
You are too bold, Bertrand. But I respect your opinion, even if it is foolish.
Bring her in!
This time I'll see the girl myself.
This better be good. I'm listening to you on faith - nothing more.
Then that is enough.
Sir, I request nothing but a horse and a few men to accompany me to see Charles VII in Chinon.

Several minutes later ...
Enough!
I still cannot believe what I'm hearing!
Voices?!
Voices tell you that you are the chosen leader to lift the siege on Orléans ...
You are dangerously close to heresy, my girl!
How can it be heresy when God himself has spoken to me through His saints? They tell me now, Captain, that you will not give me what I ask this moment. But you will, soon enough.
Joan stayed in Vaucouleurs, making an impression on everyone who met her. Many were touched by her faith and her constant presence at Mass, where she took Holy Communion and prayed fervently.

A few days later, Joan proclaimed that the French had unexpectedly defeated the English forces in the town of Rouvray. When this was confirmed, Captain de Baudricourt summoned her.
She was right! I can't believe it!
Joan, you may have what you ask. The horses and the men are yours.
Praise God! Thank you! I will leave first thing tomorrow morning!

Joan was given a horse and two escorts to accompany er to Charles VII, the heir to the throne but not yet king. In Vaucouleurs, Joan spoke boldly of her voices' latest message. Meanwhile, Charles VII anticipated her arrival vith a test to assure himself that "The Maid," as she was coming to be known, was truly hearing the voice of God.

Chinon, France. Castle of Charles VII.
See her in! I will hear for myself what this young "Maid" has come to tell me.

I am a busy man, but the village is buzzing about you, and I can no longer drown them out.
So what is it? What is it that you have come to say?
Nothing, Sir.

Nothing? Nothing?
Nothing to you, I mean.
For it is not you to whom I have been sent. You are not the king.
I am to speak with this man, the real Charles VII!

You have proved yourself, Maid, and recognized me for who I truly am! Come, let us talk!

What is this message you have come to bring me?
The voices tell me I am to lift the siege on Orléans. Then I shall accompany you to Reims where you will be crowned king of France.
How can you possibly consider this girl to lead an assault on the English at Orléans! The men will laugh in her face!
My friend, the Maid is spoken to by God! How else could she have known me?!
You must have faith! The Lord has chosen me. Your men will follow because He will make them! Don't you trust the Lord?
A good point. But we must be sure. A council will be held!
The best religious scholars will question you. If they approve that you are sent by God, I will allow you to lead French forces against the siege at Orléans!
May God be with you. We will soon see what will be done!

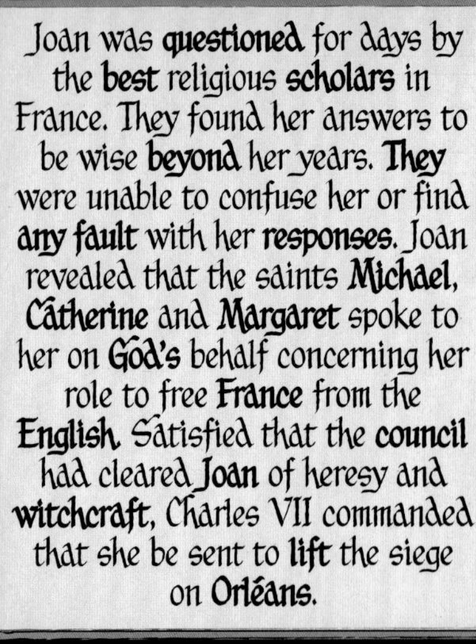
Joan was questioned for days by the best religious scholars in France. They found her answers to be wise beyond her years. They were unable to confuse her or find any fault with her responses. Joan revealed that the saints Michael, Catherine and Margaret spoke to her on God's behalf concerning her role to free France from the English. Satisfied that the council had cleared Joan of heresy and witchcraft, Charles VII commanded that she be sent to lift the siege on Orléans.

I need a sword. Go to the Church of St. Catherine in Fierbois. There you will find a sword hidden in the vault. My voices say that this is the sword I will carry throughout my service to France and to God.

I don't know of any sword buried down here!
Neither do I! She said it is buried right over here ...

I can't believe it. There it is! We must tell Charles VII at once and bring this holy Maid her sword!

To the king of England, and all others who occupy these French lands and claim them as your own ...
In the name of God, flee before Him. His servant, The Maid, will run you out of these lands to which you have no right. You have been warned.

Now that we have taken Fort Orléans, the English have retreated to Fort Augustine.
Let the soldiers rest; one fort is enough, today.
No! We must continue on!
We cannot rest. Fort Augustine must be taken! This battle is not over yet!
Where is she going? She's turned back toward the Fort! What should we do, Sir?
The Maid returns to take Fort Augustine, and so shall we! Let's ride!
For France! For God!

few days later, in Confession ...
Father, forgive me ...
Now that we have successfully taken Fort Augustine, my voices tell me it is time to attack Fort Tourelles - the strongest of all the English forts!
I ... I have horrible nightmares, of death, and flames ...

It scares me. And yet, I know I must fight, tomorrow ...
Fear not Joan, the Lord is always with you. He will give you strength for today and tomorrow.
Fort Tourelles.

Shall I signal the attack?
Yes. It's time.

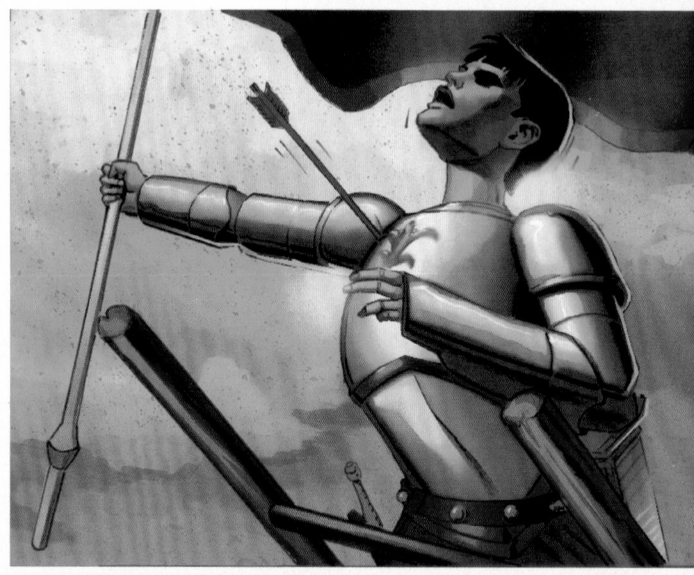

Joan! Oh, Lord please, let her live!
Is she ...?
No one could survive a fall like that.

I need to be alone!
She's alright!

She's gone to pray. I never really believed until now ...
So it's true. She really hears the voice of God!
I can only imagine what the English will say when they see her flag flying again.

Fort Tourelles
The witch is dead. I saw her fall. The French have begun to retreat. So much for this nonsense.
Umm ... Sir? I have some news ... quite astonishing, actually ...

I didn't believe it myself, Sir, until I saw her flag.
It's true! She's alive!

I don't believe it. The French ... they're attacking again!

No!!!

Joan had fulfilled her promise to Charles VII and succeeded in lifting the siege on Orléans. The people of Orléans showered her with praise and adoration and lifted their hands to touch the woman who had brought them their freedom. Joan continued to clear the path to Reims, France, by conducting many victories and freeing cities and villages from English oppression.
Soon she accompanied Charles VII to Reims, where he was finally crowned king of France.
It has been done. He is King.
So much pain and death, and now, so much waiting.
God, speak to me! Tell me what it is I should do now.

Joan spent **many** winter months with the royal court, **constantly praying** and listening for **God's w**
That **spring**, Joan defended the village **Compiègne** against the Burgundians. During the **fighting**, th
bridge was lifted, **sealing the city** and leaving Joan and many others **stranded** in **enemy territory**

Rouen, France. 1431
Joan was sold to the English as King Charles VII sat by in contemptible silence. Joan was put to trial for heresy, or holding beliefs contrary to that of the Church
Heresy was a crime punishable by death. The trial, overseen by Pierre Cauchon, the Bishop of Beauvais, consisted of months of confusion, frustration and unnecessary cruelty.
Thirty-seven judges, mostly Frenchmen from the University of Paris, looked on as prosecutors. The judges were working for the English government. They hammered Joan with questions concerning the voices she heard, the visions she saw, and her authenticity as a follower of the Word of God.

We, the court, find Joan of Arc, commonly known as The Maid, guilty of crimes of heresy.
The sentence of death stands.
She will be burned at the stake at dawn.
Dawn ... Cemetery of St-Ouen. Rouen, France. May 30, 1431.
Joan of Arc has been remembered for centuries for her constant faith, even in the face of death itself. Pius X decreed Joan's beatification in 1909 after the process was begun by the Bishop of Orléans in 1869. St. Joan of Arc was canonized by Pope Benedict XV in 1920. Joan is the patron saint of France, captives, prisoners, martyrs, soldiers and those persecuted for piety.

A Saint's Journey
1412
Joan of Arc is born to pious parents of the French peasant class near the province of Lorraine. At a very early age, she heard voices: those of St. Michael, St. Câtherine and St. Margaret.
1920
Joan is canonized a saint by Pope Benedict XV.
1460c
Joan is exonerated of all guilt.
431
oan of Arc
s burned at
he stake.
She was
only
ineteen
ears
ld.
1431
1412
1430
1428
1429
1430
Joan attempts to relieve Compéigne, but is captured by the Burgundians and sold to the English. The French did nothing to save her. After months of imprisonment, she was tried at Rouen by a tribunal. Through her unfamiliarity with the technicalities of theology, Joan was trapped into making a few damaging statements. When she refused to retract the assertion that it was the saints of God who had commanded her to do what she had done, she was condemned to death as a heretic, sorceress and adulteress.
1428
Joan of Arc hears the voices of St. Michael, St. Câtherine and St. Margaret tell her to go to the King of France and help him reconquer his kingdom. For at that time the English king was after the throne of France.
1429
After overcoming opposition from churchmen and courtiers, this seventeen year old girl was given a small army with which she raised the seige of Orléans. She then enjoyed a series of spectacular military successes, during which the King was able to enter Rheims and be crowned with her at his side.